Crissy
Family Encyclopedia
IDENTIFICATION & PRICE GUIDE
By Carla Marie Cross

Published by

Hobby House Press, Inc.
Grantsville, Maryland 21536

All photographs appearing in this book belong to the author unless otherwise specified.

Additional copies of this book may be purchased at **$24.95** (plus postage and handling) from

HOBBY HOUSE PRESS, INC.

One Corporate Drive
Grantsville, MD 21536
Call **1-800-554-1447** or fax 301-895-5029
E-mail: HYPERLINK mail to: hobbyhouse@gcnet.net hobbyhouse@gcnet.net
Or order from your favorite bookstore or dealer.

Printed in the United States of America

ISBN: 0-87588-522-5

Table of Contents

Dedication

Dedicated to everyone who remembers Crissy from the days of their childhood...

Loveliness that dies when I forget

Comes alive when I remember.

From the poem Loveliness
by Hilda Conkling

Child pictured is author's daughter Lacelynn.

A NOTE TO READERS:

Over the years I have heard from a number of collectors who have explained that the hobby of doll collecting has gotten them through some very difficult times in their lives – the loss of a spouse, child or mother. Dolls bring something to us spiritually that only those who have experienced it can understand. "Doll Hunts" are absolutely absorbing and the finds are truly rewarding. If this book or any of my writings can touch off a spark, add joy to everyday life, or comfort you in any way, then my first purpose for writing it will have been accomplished.

Your friend,

Carla Marie Cross

Acknowledgements

The following members of Crissy's extended family are to be thanked for their help with this book: Camilla Holm, Tara Wood, Paula Carranza, Pauline Yohe, Bev Hagaman, Jennifer Foster, Susan Mobley, Eugenia Kurz, Connie Ferris, Frances Waters, Wendy Werth, Doris Rickert, Jay Schefler, Cindy Sabulis, The J. Lawrence Collection.

Background on the
Ideal Toy Company

In the early 1900s a Jewish immigrant from Russia named Morris Michtom, along with his wife, opened a novelty store in Brooklyn, New York. Selling stationery, candy and playthings like the stuffed animals sewn by Mrs. Michtom, it was a small neighborhood store with no claim to fame until a certain event in 1902.

It was in November of that year that President Teddy Roosevelt traveled to Mississippi to settle a border dispute. During his stay there he decided to take a short break from business and went off to enjoy one of his favorite sports, hunting. Upon encountering a young bear cub, the President compassionately refused to shoot it. The event sparked some media interest and a cartoonist from the Washington Star, Clifford Berryman, created a cartoon celebrating the incident. The drawing was reprinted in local newspapers all over the country, and because it was associated with such a popular and engaging young President, the entire episode drew a lot of fanfare nationwide.

As his customers buzzed about it, Mr. Michtom had an inspiration. He wrote to President Roosevelt and asked his permission to use the name "Teddy" on a line of plush bears his wife would sew up and put in the windows of his little store. In true humility, President Roosevelt wrote back stating that he didn't feel his name would be worth much to the toy bear industry, but that Mr. Michtom was welcome to use it. Thus, "Teddy's Bears" began to line the shelves and windows of the small novelty shop. As their popularity swelled, the Ideal Toy Company, headed by Mr. and Mrs. Michtom, was formed to keep up with the demand.

Thus, Ideal was the manufacturer of the original Teddy Bear which was inspired by an American President. The company went on to become one of our country's leading producers of stuffed toys and dolls.

In an article on the Ideal Toy Corporation, the New York Times of Sunday, December 7, 1952, stated that: "The origin of the company is perhaps unique in American industry. It is probably the only company that ever grew directly out of a newspaper cartoon. It was the Berryman cartoon of Teddy Roosevelt refusing to shoot a bear cub which inspired ...Morris Michtom to make a Teddy Bear. This took the elder Michtom out of a confectionery business and launched him into the toy business."

After World War I, the substance of the American doll and toy industry changed drastically. "Luxury" dolls from foreign shores were not as welcome in this country as they had been before. Buyers began thumbing their noses at anything stamped "Made in Germany". Less expensive and more simply made domestic toys began to proliferate in America, and toy companies such as Ideal began to prosper.

In later years a 75 percent foreign tariff and World War II put an end to foreign domination in the American toy market.

The Ideal Toy Company actually started with their first character doll in 1907: the *Yellow Kid*, based on a character from the "Hogan's Alley" comic strip. Ideal became a pioneer in licensing the names and images of celebrities, comic characters, and advertising tie-ins. Other innovative experiments over the years were composition dolls, Mama dolls, walking dolls, two-faced dolls, and soft skin vinyl dolls. Ideal introduced sleep eyed dolls in 1915, and is credited with making the very first hard plastic doll in 1940.

Some of Ideal's "star" dolls over the years have been:

1910s

Mr. Hooligan, Water Baby, Baby Mine, Dandy Kid, Ty Cobb, Captain Jinks, Naughty Marietta, Freddie and Flora, Tiny Toddler, Country Cousins, Baby Bettie, Sleep-Eye babies (Paula, Lolo, Bunting, etc.), *Dottie Dimples, Farmer Kids, Baby Talc, Sanitary Baby, Prize Baby,* and bent-limb babies such as *Old Glory Kids* and *Baby Bi-Face.*

Ideal dolls in this era were made by a patented "Skeleton Process" and of a material called composition, claimed to be both unbreakable and washable. Benjamin Michtom, Morris' son, stated that their composition was made from flour, glue and two other ingredients (probably sawdust and water). It was advertised at this time that their composition dolls could be dropped from an eight story window to the pavement below without scratching the paint, and that these precious little dolls were durable enough to drive nails!

Cost of the Ideal dolls of this era was in the range of 25 cents to three dollars.

1920s

Mama dolls, Soozie Smiles (with two faces), *Surprise Baby* (with two faces and two voices), *Beau Brummel, Flossie Flirt, Carrie Joy, Hush-A-Bye Baby* (Ideal's answer to Grace Storey Putnam's *Bye Lo Baby*), *Tickle Toes,* and *Peter Pan.*

Original prices for Ideal dolls in the 1920s were between $1.50 and $15.00.

1930s

Shirley Temple, Deanna Durbin, Judy Garland, Fanny Brice, Snoozie, Nancy Lee, Snow White, Gabby, Ticklette (baby sister to *Tickle Toes*) and the Honeysuckle line.

1940s

Magic Skin babies, *Betty Jane, Honey Baby,* Flexy character dolls, *Baby Beautiful, Queen of the Ice* (probably skating along on Sonja Henie's popularity) and *Plassie.*

1950s

Thrift kit dolls (made for penny-conscious Moms to hand string and sew for), *Mary Hartline, Baby Coos, Sara Lee, Pete* and *Repete, Snookie, Baby Ruth, Kiss Me* character babies (also known as "Blessed Event"), and the hugely popular *Saucy Walker, Toni, Betsy McCall,* and *Miss Revlon* (teen doll predecessors to BARBIE®.

1960s

An explosion of baby boomer favorites including the *Patty Playpal* family, *Thumbelina, Tubsy, Kissy, Giggles,* 42-inch tall *Daddy's Girl,* 25-inch tall *Bye Bye Baby, Posie, Bonnie Baby, Cream Puff, Goody Two Shoes, Katie Kachoo, Miss Ideal, Betsy Wetsy, Teary Dearie,* and of course, the *Tammy* family, which included boyfriend and an entire family (Mom, Dad, sister *Pepper,* brothers *Ted* and *Pete,* and several others). *Tammy* was one of the few BARBIE® competitors that gained true popularity in her own right.

1970s

New issue of *Tiny Tears,* originally manufactured by American Character, the most unique *Flatsy* dolls, *Belly Button Baby,* and of course, the *Crissy* family of dolls, subject of this book!

Crissy

An early *Crissy*.

There are few things in life that have the allure of long hair on a female. It is, in its very nature, eye-catching and elegant. It has color, sheen, movement, shape and texture. Soldiers carried long locks of women's hair into battle as early as the Middle Ages. In ancient Scotland, long hair on a woman was considered so powerful, that women were ordered to cover it from sight. It was believed that if a woman with long hair shook it at you, it would cause anything from bad luck to death.

The late 1960s and early 1970s in this country was certainly a time in which long hair was enjoying immense popularity. The Broadway musical *Hair* screamed to the lyrics "...no words for the beauty, the splendor, the wonder of my hair...flow it, show it, long as I can grow it – my hair!" From junior high age to young adults, the fashion was wearing hair long and straight. Combined with the natural delirium that little girls have with combing and fussing over their dolls' hair, this was the perfect time for *Crissy* to make her appearance on the doll market. Not since Ideal's 1950's *Toni,* had a doll's central theme revolved around hairstyling.

No other major doll before her had hair quite like this! The very first *Crissy,* brought out in 1969, had a generous head of hair that streamed down to the floor and

Crissy Fact:

Crissy was named *"Beautiful Crissy"* by Ideal, her manufacturer, but is known simply as *Crissy* to collectors, which is how she will be referred to in this book.

A later *Crissy*.

beyond! To add to *Crissy's* originality, her hair was red! A glossy combination of warm cinnamon and garnets, it caused her to stand out in the sea of platinum blondes we were all swimming in at the time. Another outstanding trait – her brown eyes. Incredibly large and gorgeous, they are beautifully shaped and her most noticeable feature.

Without a doubt, her biggest selling point was the grow-hair mechanism Ideal placed in the torso of each doll. Ideal's grow-hair dolls, with the exception of *Baby Crissy,* have a button in their front abdomen that, when depressed, releases a long ponytail to the desired length. A knob in the doll's back winds the hair back into her head. A true novelty, this device made *Crissy* family dolls top sellers!

Crissy also offered a bit of distinction in the age she asserted to be. Mattel's *BARBIE*®, however old you would have her to be in your imaginative play, was fully matured. Mattel's *Skipper* (*BARBIE*®'s little sister) was just entering adolescence. Perhaps riding the crest of *Francie*'s (*BARBIE*®'s cousin) popularity. *Crissy* was somewhere in between with a somewhat developed body, but not fully developed. *Crissy* had a more mature line of clothing than many dolls, but never vampy or ultra-sophisticated. She was a combination of characteristics that made her exceptional, and ultimately, in demand.

At left, first issue *Crissy* (1968-69) wears an orange lace mini dress and orange shoes. Her hair is floor-length or longer, which is a distinction that sets her apart from later issues. At right, *Black Crissy* wears an apple green replica of the lace dress, has striking jet black hair, and was produced later, closer to 1970. *Photo courtesy of Bev Hagaman.*

Close-up of the first issue *Black Crissy* with floor-length hair.

Second issue *Crissy*, from about 1969, is the same as the first issue, but with knee-length hair. It also came as an African-American doll. *Photo courtesy of Tara Wood and Paula Carranza.*

Third issue *Crissy,* 1969-70, wears a turquoise silk-type fabric mini dress and matching shoes. She is the same as the second issue *Crissy,* only the dress is different. No African-American version of this doll was made. *Photo courtesy of Tara Wood and Paula Carranza.*

Movin' Groovin' Crissy came in an orange midi dress and orange boots. This was the first *Crissy* to have a posing waist. A pull string mechanism operated the moving portion of her body, which was above her waist. *Photo courtesy of Bev Hagaman.*

Movin' Groovin' Crissy, from 1971, came in both white and African-American versions. Two of the dolls pose by their original box. *Photo courtesy of Tara Wood and Paula Carranza.*

Talky Crissy is described as being able to say 12 different sentences. Some collectors have *Talky Crissys* that say only six. She came with the following accessories: velvet ribbons, bobby pins, brush and curlers.

Talky Crissy from 1971 is distinguished by a thick torso that housed a voice box. This doll was a pull string talker. One version had a pull string in her back, another version had the pull string in her side. The pull string in the back is very hard to find; some collectors consider it a rarity. The end of the pull string had a stylish plastic butterfly instead of the usual ring. *Photo courtesy of Bev Hagaman.*

The hair of *Talky Crissy* is different than the previous *Crissy*s. The top hair is shorter on the sides and her bangs are thinner. *Talky Crissy* is described as being able to say 12 different sentences. Some collectors have *Talky Crissy* dolls that say only six sentences. *Photo courtesy of Tara Wood and Paula Carranza.*

Crissy Fact:

Early *Crissy* dolls had darker and heavier eyeliner, and often had a slightly darker skin tone than the later *Crissy*s. They also had straighter top hair than the later *Crissy* dolls.

View of the pull string mechanism. *Photo courtesy of Tara Wood and Paula Carranza.*

Talky Crissy came in a long pink satin robe that had an eyelet to accommodate the butterfly on the pull string, and pink shoes.

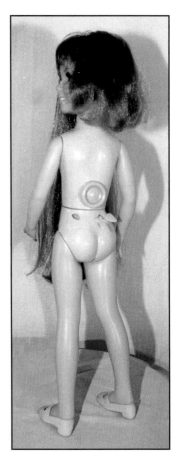

Look Around Crissy's head and upper body turns from side to side when the pull string is extended. *Photo courtesy Tara Woods and Paula Carranza.*

Look Around Crissy, from 1972, came wearing a green plaid taffeta maxi dress and green shoes. She has less face makeup than former *Crissy* dolls and her top hair has a slight curl. Head and upper body turns from side to side when the pull string is extended. *Photo courtesy of Tara Woods and Paula Carranza.*

Crissy Fact:

The very first issue *Crissy*s, with the floor length hair, often have a hair texture that is more easily tangled and harder to work with than the second issue *Crissy* dolls and beyond which had knee length hair. A bit of spray furniture polish can help untangle *Crissy*'s hair.

Look Around Crissy with the original box.

The African-American version of *Look Around Crissy*. *Photo courtesy of Jennifer Foster.*

Swirla Curler Crissy, from 1973, came packaged wearing an orangish-red plaid jumper with a holly sprig on the left shoulder, a matching red-orange blouse and shoes. As with *Look Around Crissy*, the hair is curlier and there is less make-up than previous *Crissy* dolls. *Swirla Curler Crissy* came with a unique apparatus for her hair, as shown on the box front. *Photo courtesy of Tara Wood and Paula Carranza.*

13

Swirla Curler Crissy was available in both white and African-American versions.

Twirly Beads Crissy, from 1974, was dressed in a bright pink gingham country-style maxi dress, which illustrates perfectly the change in fashion trends from 1968 to 1974. She came with white shoes and strands of pink and white beads to be used as hair decorations. She has curlier hair and less makeup, like the *Crissy* dolls made after 1972. The mint example pictured has the gorgeous coloring typical of these later dolls. *Photo courtesy of Tara Wood and Paula Carranza.*

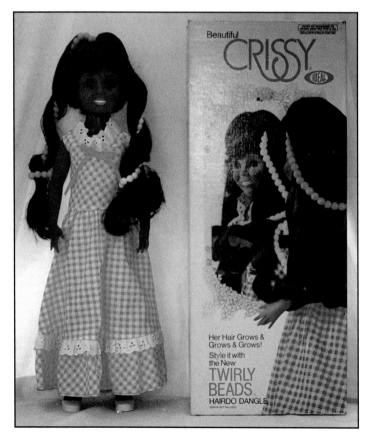

The African-American version of *Twirly Beads Crissy. Photo courtesy of Jennifer Foster.*

Magic Hair Crissy appeared in 1977, after a three year intermission when no new *Crissy* dolls were issued. *Magic Hair Crissy* bears very little resemblance to her predecessors. With a completely new face mold, she had no grow hair feature, but came with five hair pieces, that attached to her head by means of "magic dots" that were made of Velcro. *Photo courtesy of Jay Schefler.*

Made in both white and African-American versions, *Magic Hair Crissy* had painted eyes and wore a pink midi skirt and white camisole top. *Photos courtesy of Jay Schefler.*

New Issue Crissy, from 1983, is 15-1/2-inches tall with a Velvet-style body and face, but *Crissy*'s coloring. The new *Crissy* came in a white cotton sundress with lace trim and white T-strap shoes. *Photo courtesy of Tara Wood and Paula Carranza.*

Crissy **Fact:**

New Issue *Crissy* dolls from 1983 are the same dolls as the first *Velvet* dolls, but with a different skin tone and a pull string instead of a knob.

New Issue *Country Fashion Crissy*, from 1983, was the same doll as New Issue Crissy, but in a different dress. The outfit was either a lavender and white checked or mauve and white checked long skirt with suspenders, a rosebud print blouse, and white T-strap shoes and a straw hat. *Photo courtesy of Tara Wood and Paula Carranza.*

New Issue Crissy also came in an African-American version. *Photo courtesy of Jay Schefler.*

White new issue *Crissy* dolls have been found with brown, violet, and amber eyes. This doll has the violet eyes. *Photo courtesy of Jay Schefler.*

Here is a comparison between a New Issue *Crissy* from 1983 on the left and the first *Velvet* on the right. They are obviously the same doll and came in both white and African-American versions.

Offered in 1980 by Dollspart Supply Company's catalog, the Porcelain *Crissy* offers a most unique addition to any *Crissy* collection. Listed as 18in (46cm) tall, she sold for $300. And was dressed in the first issue orange lace dress and orange shoes.

The New Issue *Crissy* dolls can be distinguished from older *Velvet* dolls by a difference in skin color and a pull string, rather than a knob as part of their grow hair device. The African-American New Issue *Crissy*, on the left, has a grayer or taupe tone to her skin, while the first *Velvet*, on the right, has warmer gold undertones. The grow hair mechanisms in their backs are pictured.

Crissy **Fact:**

Crissy dolls have a graceful "fanned out" position to their fingers, similar to what were called "ballet fingers" in early dance classes. Although this is a beautiful detail to the doll, it can be a source of frustration in trying to fit their hands through the often very narrow sleeves of many of *Crissy*'s garments.

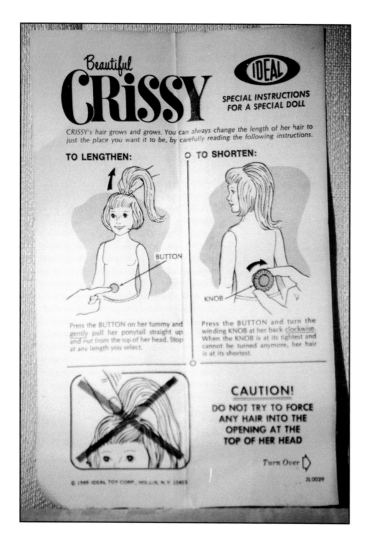

The front of a *Crissy* box insert which gives instructions on how to change the length of *Crissy*'s hair.

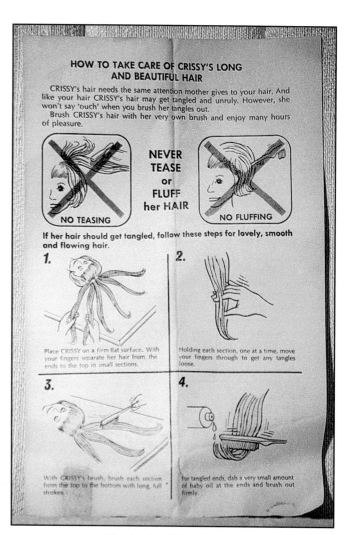

The back of the box insert explains how to untangle *Crissy*'s long hair.

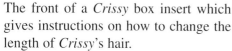

A letter to the mother who bought *Crissy* for her daughter also was a box insert.

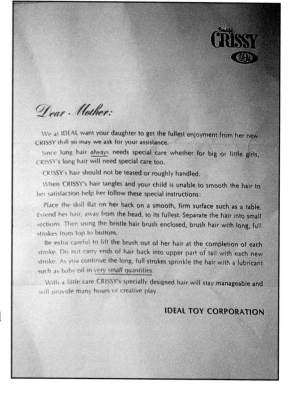

The letter explained how to mother and care for *Crissy*'s hair.

Baby Crissy

Within doll collections, there are always certain groups or categories of dolls that have worked their way into the collector's heart and become his or her favorites. The 11-1/2in (29cm) fashion dolls are favored by many collectors. The tiny *Ginnette*-type babies or 8in (20cm) toddler dolls like *Ginny* are held dear by many others.

For those collectors who specifically love life-size baby dolls, *Baby Crissy* has always been a favorite. An entire collector's club and newsletter sprang up around these "Big Babies Beautiful" in the 1980s, with some members collecting even hospital mannequins. One of the most appealing qualities of these "large as life" dolls is that they can be dressed up in real baby clothes, for which the selection is almost endless.

Baby Crissy was born in 1973 and was meant to depict how *Crissy* would have looked as a baby. A large 24in (61cm), she had an engaging chubbiness about her and had the same coloring as *Crissy*. Her grow hair mechanism operated from a pull string instead of the usual button/knob device.

Her first issue outfit was a pink two-piece dress with a lace-trimmed Peter Pan collar and two pockets. A variation of this same outfit came out in salmon colored later that year, and in lavender in 1975.

First *Baby Crissy*, from 1973, came in a pink two-piece dress. *Photo courtesy of Wendy Werth.*

The second *Baby Crissy* was the same as the first issue, except it wore a different outfit, a white sunsuit. The white doll's sunsuit was trimmed in green gingham. *Photo courtesy of Tara Wood and Paula Carranza.*

The African-American version of the second *Baby Crissy* wore a white sunsuit trimmed in yellow gingham. *Photo courtesy of Tara Wood and Paula Carranza.*

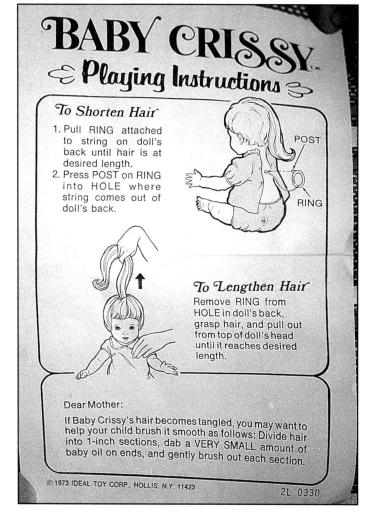

Baby Crissy came with instructions explaining how to work her pull string mechanism.

A comparison of the two versions of *Baby Crissy* shows that the one from the 1980s, on the left, is made of a more rigid vinyl than the original *Baby Crissy*. The original *Baby Crissy* dolls have cheeks, arms and legs that can be "squished" and have an overall larger or rounder appearance than the later issue dolls. The cheek blush and total skin coloring of the later issue dolls are found in less faded condition than the earlier dolls. The same phenomena occurred with Mattel's *Chatty Cathy* dolls. When the face molds were changed from the soft to the harder vinyl, the doll's faces became smaller and retained their color better. It is not uncommon to find these later issue *Baby Crissy* dolls with one soft and one hard leg.

This hairless *Baby Crissy* was made by CBS Toys in 1983. Although she bears no resemblance to any other *Baby Crissy*, she is a high quality, beautiful, classic baby doll in her own right. At 17in (43cm) tall, she is a drink and wet nurser, all-vinyl with great eye and skin coloring. Her wrist tag reads "Mommies who know and loved our fine dolls when they were small know the care and craftsmanship that go into every Ideal doll." *Doll courtesy of Pauline Yohe*.

Some of the classic Ideal dolls were reissued in 1991 under the title of "Ideal Nursery" dolls. Here, in a denim jumper is the Ideal *Nursery Baby Crissy* with the grow hair feature and black eyes. Ideal Nursery dolls were produced by Tyco. *Photo courtesy of Wendy Werth*.

Talking Baby Crissy from the 1991 Ideal Nursery group is a 17in (43cm) doll with the grow hair feature and a talking mechanism. These dolls, manufactured by Tyco, had brown eyes and were later sold without the talking mechanism. This photograph compares the packaging of the *Talking Baby Crissy* on the left with the doll without the voice box on the right.

Ideal Nursery outfits suitable for Ideal *Nursery Baby Crissy* from the early 1990s. *Photo courtesy of Wendy Werth.*

Now called "Playtime Nursery" and manufactured by Tyco in 1995, is *Beauty Parlor Baby Crissy* with a grow hair feature. The white version has bright green eyes. *Photo courtesy of Wendy Werth.*

In 1991 four versions of *Teeny Baby Crissy* were issued under the name Ideal Nursery. All had grow hair features. Manufactured by Tyco, the white version has blue eyes and the African-American version has brown eyes. *Photo courtesy of Wendy Werth.*

The back of the *Beauty Parlor Baby Crissy* doll box shows some of the other dolls that were issued as part of the "Classic Doll Collection": *Rub-A-Dub Dolly* (originally from 1975), *Tiny Tears* (originally 1950s and 60s), and *Betsy Wetsy* (originally 1950s).

A close-up shows Beauty *Parlor Baby Crissy*'s bright green eyes.

Beauty Parlor Baby Crissy is beginning to arouse some interest among collectors because of her unique pale green eyes and pastel reddish hair.

Velvet

Crissy's younger cousin made her appearance in 1970. Named *Velvet*, she was dressed in a velvet jumper with a big satin bow and had, like *Crissy*, striking coloring and large expressive eyes. A beautiful silvery blonde, she had violet eyes. Because this eye color was rarely seen on dolls, purple of all shades became her signature color and can be seen throughout her wardrobe and in her accessories. She stands 15-1/2in (39cm) tall and has a hair growth mechanism which extends her ponytail to about knee length. *Velvet* is marked "1969 IDEAL TOY CORP/GH-15-H-157" on her head and "1970 IDEAL TOY CORP/GH-15 2M516901" on her back. All *Velvets* in this chapter are 15-1/2in (39cm) tall unless otherwise noted.

Her debut dress, a dark purple velvet jumper was later changed to a waleless corduroy jumper of the same design.

Velvet has an impish expression. She was also easy for children to dress and handle.

A close-up of *Velvet*'s large violet eyes.

The first *Velvet*, in 1969 and 1970, came in a purple velvet jumper. Later issues of *Velvet* came in a purple waleless corduroy jumpers. *Photo courtesy of Tara Wood and Paula Carranza.*

Velvet's two jumpers: the first version in velvet is on the left, and the later corduroy version is on the right.

As with *Crissy*, Ideal waited to see how successful *Velvet* would be before manufacturing an African-American counterpart in 1970-71. The African-American version came in a lavender corduroy jumper and lavender shoes. *Photo courtesy of Bev Hagaman.*

Movin' Groovin' Velvet in 1971 had the same "movin'" mechanism as *Movin' Groovin' Crissy*. She came in a two-tone pink, dropped waist dress, with purple bows in her hair and on the front of the dress skirt, and purple T-strap shoes. *Movin' Groovin' Velvet* also came in an African-American version. *Photo courtesy of Tara Wood and Paula Carranza.*

A close-up of *Movin' Grovin' Velvet*'s dress from the 1970-71 period.

Talky Velvet, from 1971 had a larger torso, like *Talky Crissy*, to house the voice box. This doll came dressed in a yellow quilted robe, yellow shoes, and a hair bow. *Photo courtesy of Tara Wood and Paula Carranza.*

Talky Velvet is described as saying six different things. She came with velvet ribbons and curlers. *Photo courtesy of Tara Wood and Paula Carranza.*

A close-up of *Talky Velvet*'s robe.

Look Around Velvet, from 1972 was dressed in a red plaid taffeta dress and red or white shoes. A pull string activated the moving apparatus as with *Look Around Crissy*. An African-American version was also made. *Photo courtesy of Tara Wood and Paula Carranza.*

Beauty Braider Velvet from 1973 came dressed in a white cotton mini dress with a lavender flower print and light purple shoes. She came with a lavender braiding device for her ponytail. (See the chapter on original catalog ads.) *Photo courtesy of Bev Hagaman.*

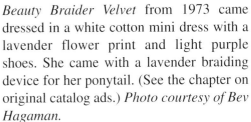

An African-American *Beauty Braider Velvet* was also available. The photograph shows her braiding attachment. *Photo courtesy of Jennifer Foster.*

Front view of the *Velvet Beauty Braider* box. *Photo courtesy of Jennifer Foster.*

Back view of the box explains how to use *Velvet's Beauty Braider*. *Photo courtsey of Jennifer Foster.*

Swirly Daisies Velvet from 1974 came dressed in a purple, pink and green plaid dress with a white yoke, lavender shoes and a daisy chain for her hair. In this picture she poses with two *Movin' Groovin' Velvet* dolls. *Photo courtesy of Bev Hagaman.*

Swirly Daisies Velvet with a *Tressy*. *Photo courtesy of Tara Wood and Paula Carranza.*

30

Swirly Daisies Velvet with her original box. *Photo courtesy of Jennifer Foster.*

The African-American version of *Swirly Daisies Velvet* and her original box. *Photo courtesy of Jennifer Foster.*

New issue *Velvet* from the 1980s came dressed in the same dress as the new issue *Crissy*. She has beautiful coloring with platinum hair and deep violet eyes. *Photo courtesy of Jay Schefler.*

Cinnamon

Cinnamon was a real individual within the *Crissy* family. At 11-1/2in (29cm), she couldn't share clothes with any of the other *Crissy* family dolls. She was one of the few with painted, rather than sleep eyes, and had her truly unique shade of hair. More of a toddler than a little girl or teenager, she boasts a really winning face, with great mouth sculpting – bright, appealing eyes – and the perfect button nose!

Cinnamon shows off her glinting head of hair, a unique shade of pastel copper.

First *Cinnamon* – known only as *Velvet's* Little Sister appeared in 1971. Truly adorable, *Velvet's* little sister was the same doll that was later to be called *Cinnamon*. With more of a chubby toddler-type body, she stood 11-1/2in (29cm) tall, and had beautiful hair that was a unique shade of pastel copper, and painted blue eyes. She was very hard to resist! This first issue wore a dropped-waist dress of orange and white dot fabric, with matching shorts underneath, and orange T-strap shoes with squared-off toes. She was available only as a white doll. *Photo courtesy of Jennifer Foster.*

Velvet's Little Sister in her original plastic wrap with her original box. *Photo courtesy of Jennifer Foster.*

Second *Cinnamon* debuted in 1973 with her unique hair doodler. This version of *Cinnamon* had a string device that pulled her hair into a mass of curls. A small cone was hidden in her hair, while a barrette and a ring, each on a string, pulled her hair into the curly style. The orange and white

fabric of her dress was the same as the *Velvet's* Little Sister doll, but this time she wore a smock top (all the rage in 1973), shorts, and the same orange T-strap shoes. *Photo courtesy of Tara Wood and Paula Carranza.*

The second version of *Cinnamon* also came in an African-American version. *Photo courtesy of Tara Wood and Paula Carranza.*

The box of the second *Cinnamon* carried instructions on how to use the hairdoodler.

A close-up of the graphics on the *Cinnamon* "Hairdoodler" box. The price tag on the upper right hand corner reads $6.99.

The African-American *Cinnamon* with hairdoodler. *Photo courtesy of Bev Hagaman.*

A brochure was provided with the *Cinnamon* doll that came with the hairdoodler to clear up the mystery of just how this apparatus worked.

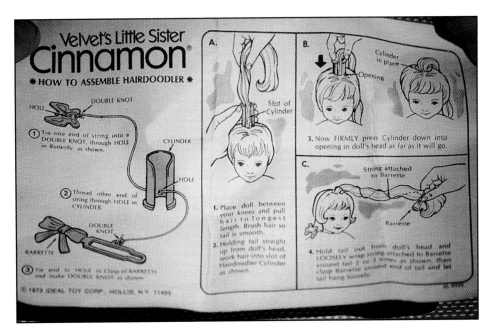

Third *Cinnamon*, with curly ribbons apeared in 1974. This *Cinnamon* was dressed in the same outfit as the second issue, but came with an extra outfit – blue denim bib shorts, yellow and white checked shirt, and blue shoes. It was made as both a white and an African-American doll. It is thought that some of the black dolls came only in the bib shorts, with no extra orange outfit. Curly ribbon *Cinnamon* came with white and yellow plastic hair ribbons. *Photo courtesy of Jennifer Foster.*

Four outfits have been listed for *Cinnamon*:
#8284-4 Pink Fleece Pajamas
#8185-1 White Overalls
#8186-9 Two-piece Playsuit with long pants
#8187-7 Aqua Dress

Cinnamon (1971-1974) shows off her adorable chubby knees in the bib shorts and checcked shirt that came with curly ribbon *Cinnamon.*

Three versions of *Cinnamon* in mint and original outfits. *Photo courtesy of Bev Hagaman.*

Crissy's Friends

Tressy

Kerry

Brandi

Harmony

Tressy

Crissy's friend *Tressy* was brought out in 1969, another striking doll with exceptional coloring. She was 17-1/2in (45cm) tall, with deep black hair, vivid blue eyes and pale lip color. Similar to Mattel's *Casey* doll, *Tressy's* facial sculpting and features were somewhat bolder, rounder, more pronounced. This gave her a character and individuality, traits common throughout the *Crissy* family. All *Tressy* dolls were Sears Exclusives.

Tressy had remarkable blue eyes and striking black hair.

First *Tressy* came out in 1969. She wore a gold and white Hawaiian print mini dress and orange shoes. Tressy was available as both African-American and white dolls through Sears. A hair kit was included as a bonus. *Photo courtesy Bev Hagaman.*

Tressy's original box pictured how her hair grew from short to long. *Photo courtesy of Bev Hagaman.*

The African-American version of *Tressy* in her original Hawaiian print dress. *Photo courtesy of Bev Hagaman.*

Some of the first *Tressy* dolls came with this yellow stretch headband.

The second *Tressy* arrived in 1971. The Sears catalog listed this second issue as *Movin' Groovin" Tressy*, but her box was labeled *Posin' Tressy*. With a bit more lip color, she is about the same doll as the first *Tressy*, but with a poseable waist. She came dressed in an aqua satin mini dress with sheer lace sleeves and aqua shoes. No African-American version was made of this second issue. A special bride dress and veil was made for *Tressy* (or any similar 17-1/2in [45cm] doll) by Sears in 1972 and sold for at least three years. *Photo courtesy of Bev Hagaman.*

Kerry

Kerry, "*Crissy*'s Irish Cousin", 17-1/2in (45cm) tall, was brought out in 1971. With sea-mist green sleep eyes, pearl blonde hair and perfect features, she is one of Ideal's most beautiful modern dolls. She was available only as a white doll. *Kerry* has a straight body and is marked "©1970/Ideal Toy Corp/ HGH-18-H-172/ Hong Kong/18 EYE" on her head. Her back was marked: "1969/ Ideal Toy Corp/ GH-18/U.S. Pat/ #3,162,976". She came in an unusual green and yellow elephant-print romper and green Mary Jane shoes.

Kerry in her original outfit beside her box. As with Tomy's *Kimberly*, her blonde hair is almost blinding in the light. When found in mint condition, these *Kerry* dolls, like others in the *Crissy* family, have a jarring beauty.

This close-up of *Kerry* shows her unusual eye color.

Brandi

Brandi, "*Crissy*'s California Cousin" that appeared in 1972, has a bit of added intrigue to offer collectors – she came in more than one hair color. Ideal may have been doing some experimenting, because *Brandi* is found in varying shades of blonde, including ash, golden, and platinum. She is 17-1/2in (45cm) tall and has electric blue eyes and a serious tan.

Brandi was supposedly representing California culture in 1972. She has those "oh-so-70's" side braids, a bright tangerine lace-up swimsuit to match her tangerine lace-up clogs, and a heart tatoo under her right eye. If you can see past the faddishness, she is a beautiful doll - another masterwork of coloring. *Brandi* had painted eyes, a poseable waist and was only made as a white doll.

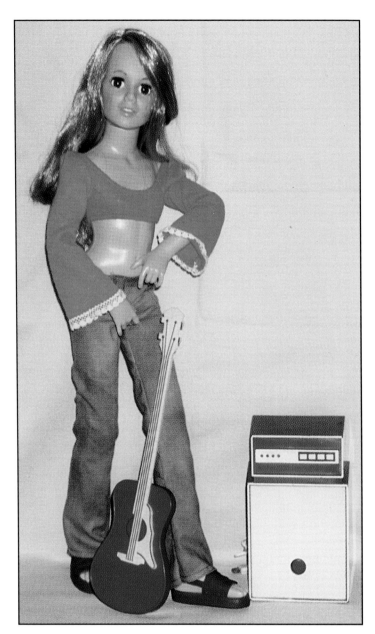

Harmony

Although she is not a grow hair doll, *Harmony*, made by Ideal in 1972, is considered part of the *Crissy* family by most collectors. Her large brown eyes and glossy hair definitely give her that family resemblance, but *Harmony* has her own unique characteristics that make her distinctly different from other family members.

Here she is shown in her hip-hugger out-fit. *Photo courtesy of J. Lawrence collection.*

Harmony, 21in (53cm) tall, came with her own guitar, amplifier and record and could sway back and forth to the beat of the music. She came dressed in a very BARBIE® Quick Curl©-style dress and sandals. Her outfits, called her "Hear and Wear Hits" each came with an additional two-song record that could be played on her amplifier. *Photo courtesy of J. Lawrence collection.*

Harmony's mint-in-package hip-hugger outfit, consisting of pants, midriff top and neck scarf. *Photo courtesy of J. Lawrence collection.*

Another *Harmony* "Hear 'n Wear" outfit is the bikini with lace cover up. *Photo courtesy of J. Lawrence collection.*

Harmony's patchwork maxi jumper is shown in the original packaging. *Photo courtesy of J. Lawrence collection.*

Velvet's Friends

Mia

Cricket

Dina

Tara

Mia

Mia, one of *Velvet*'s little playmates, arrived on the scene in 1971.

With a "pixie-ish" look, and a dead ringer for Sally Field, she had large bright blue sleep eyes, dark brown hair, and a straight body. She is marked "13 EYE" on the head and "GH 15/ 2M 5169-01" on the back. *Mia*, like *Velvet*, is 15in (38cm) tall and was made only as a white doll. Her original outfit was a light blue bubble suit and blue T-strap shoes.

Mia poses in her original outfit beside her original box. The doll pictured is unusual in that her hair is about three inches longer than the knee-length style. *Photo courtesy of Tara Wood and Paula Carranza.*

Cricket

The first *Cricket* was sold in 1971.

A close-up of the first and most common *Cricket,* with brown eyes.

Although the Sears catalog dubbed her *Movin' Groovin' Cricket,* Ideal labeled her box as *Posin' Cricket.* At 15-1/2in (39cm) tall, she was considered one of *Velvet's* friends. Another radiant redhead, she was made only as a white doll and usually had brown sleep eyes. Her original dress was an orange and white diagonal check with a dropped waist look and orange T-strap shoes. *Photo courtesy of Tara Wood and Paula Carranza.*

Blue-eyed *Cricket* came out in 1972. Sears offered *Cricket* in her usual orange checked dress, but a blue floor-length dress was also offered along with the doll. The only unusual point in these later issue *Cricket*s is that some of them were made with blue eyes. Blue-eyed *Cricket* is extremely hard to find and is very much sought after by collectors. *Photo courtesy of Bev Hagaman.*

Dina

Dina was introduced in 1972 as *Brandi*'s little sister and another California cousin of *Crissy*'s.

Dina sported the same deep tanned skin and sun-streaked hair as *Brandi*. At 15-1/2in (39cm) tall, she could wear *Velvet*'s clothes – that is, if she wanted to. Some of *Velvet*'s more traditional school and party dresses may not have gone too well with *Dina*'s leg tattoo or her overall California image.

Dina had a poseable waist, painted eyes, and was made only as a white doll. She came in lavender bibs and white lace-up clogs and has only been found, to my knowledge, as a platinum blonde. Her butterfly tattoo was different from *Brandi*'s in that it came in her box and was meant to be placed on her leg by her new owner rather than applied directly to the doll in the factory. She is often found without her tattoo, as it could very well have fallen off during play.

Two of the "funkier" outfits pictured on *Dina* and *Brandi* boxes.

The introduction of *Brandi* and *Dina* seemed to usher in a new "funkier" phase in *Crissy* and *Velvet* outfits. The outfits that Ideal featured on the sides of *Dina* and *Brandi* boxes, like "Hippy Happening", "Funky Feathers", "Burlap Bag", and "Cloud Movements" were highly creative and campier than the outfits that preceded them.

47

Tara

Tara, new in 1976, was a pioneer in her day since she was made with more realistic ethnic features than the African-American dolls that preceded her.

Note that *Tara* is harder to find than other members of the *Crissy* family.

Some collectors may argue that *Tara* is not officially a member of the *Crissy* family, as there is no mention of the *Crissy* family on her box or papers. However, with her body mold, grow hair feature, and overall appeal, she should consider herself adopted!

A 15-1/2in (38cm) friend of *Velvet*'s, she came in a bright yellow checked pants suit and bright yellow T-strap shoes. With prominent lip color and cheek blush, she really stands out in the crowds of dolls on the shelves at antique malls and tables at flea markets. *Photo courtesy of Tara Wood and Paula Carranza.*

Chart of
Crissy Family Dolls

If you find one of the *Crissy* dolls without her box or original clothing, the following chart can help you figure out which one you have!

Doll	Stationary Eyes	Sleep Eyes	Painted Eyes	Posable Waist	Straight Body	Grow Hair Device	Marks	Black Doll Made
1st & 2nd Issue *Crissy*		X			X	Yes	©1968/Ideal Toy Corp./ GH-17-H129 (on head) ©1969 Ideal Toy Corp / GH-18 US PAT. 3,162,976 (on back)	Yes
3rd Issue *Crissy*		X			X	Yes	Same as 1st & 2nd Issue	No
Movin' Groovin' Crissy		X		X		Yes	1968 / Ideal Toy Corp / GH-17-H-129 (on head) 1971/ Ideal Toy Corp / M6-18 2M-53-13-02 (on back)	Yes
Talky Crissy (with side butterfly)		X			X	Yes	1968 / Ideal Toy Corp. / GH-17-H-129 (on head) Ideal Toy Corp 1970/ U.S. Pat. 3162976 / Other Pats. Pend. (on back)	No
Look Around Crissy		X			X	Yes	1968 / Ideal Toy Corp. / GH-18-H129 (on head) 1972 Ideal Toy Corp. / Hong Kong / US Pat. No. 3162976 / Other Pats Pending (on back)	Yes
Swirla Curler Crissy		X			X	Yes	101 OR 45 / Hong Kong / ©1968 / Ideal Toy Corp. / GH-17-H129 (on head) Made in Hong Kong / ©1969 Ideal Toy Corp. / GH 18 (on back)	Yes
Twirly Bead Crissy		X			X	Yes	Same as *Swirla Curler Crissy*	Yes
Magic Hair Crissy			X		X	No	1977 / Ideal Toy Corp. / M.H.C. –19-H-281 / Hong Kong (on head) 1974/Ideal / Hollis NY 11423 / 2-M-285-01 (on back)	Yes
New Issue *Crissy*		X			X	Yes	13 EYE / 02 / ©1969 / Ideal Toy Corp / GH-15-H-157 (on head) ©1970 Ideal Toy Corp / GH-15 / 2M5 169-01 (on back) (same head and body as 1st *Velvet*, but with a pull string instead of a knob)	Yes
Baby Crissy	X				X	Yes	1972 Ideal Toy Corp. / GHB-H-226 (on head) ©1973 / Ideal Toy Corp. / 2M-5611 / 7 (on back)	Yes
Baby Crissy (Reissue 1983)	X				X	Yes	©1972 / Ideal Toy Corp / GHB-H-225 (on neck) ©1973 / Ideal Toy Corp. / GHB / M8H-01 (on back)	Yes
Harmony		X			X		H-2000 / 1971 Ideal (on head) 1972 / Ideal Toy Corp (on back)	No
First *Velvet*		X			X	Yes	3 EYE / ©1969 / Ideal Toy Corp / GH-15-H-157 (on neck) ©1970 / Ideal Toy Corp. / GH-15 / 2M5 169-01 (on back)	Yes
Movin' Groovin' Velvet		X		X		Yes	13 EYE ©1969 / Ideal Toy Corp / GH-15-H-157 (on neck) ©1971 / Ideal Toy Corp / MG-15 / US Pat 3,162,9761 / Other Pat Pend (on upper back) ©1971 / Ideal Toy Corp / M-15 / 2M-5317-02/1 (on back)	Yes
Talky Velvet		X			X	Yes	1969 / Ideal Toy Corp / GH-15-H-157 (on head) ©1971 / Ideal Toy Corp / TV 15 ? US Pat. 3162975 / Other Patents Pend (on back)	Yes

Doll	Stationary Eyes	Sleep Eyes	Painted Eyes	Posable Waist	Straight Body	Grow Hair Device	Marks	Black Doll Made
Look Around Velvet		X			X	Yes	©1969 / Ideal Toy Corp / GH-15-H-157 / Hong Kong (on neck) ©1972 Ideal Toy Corp / Hong Kong P. / US Pat No 3,162,976 / Other Patents Pending (on back)	**Yes**
Beauty Braider Velvet		X			X	Yes	1969 / Ideal Toy Corp / GH 15-H-157 (on head)1970 / Ideal Toy Corp / GH-15-2M 5196-01 (on back)	**Yes**
Swirly Daisy Velvet		X			X	Yes	1969 Ideal Toy Corp. / GH-15-H-157 (on neck) 1970 Ideal Toy Corp./ GH-15 2M 516 901 (on back)	**Yes**
1st *Cinnamon*			X			Yes	1971 Ideal Toy Corp. / GH-12-H-183 Hong Kong (on neck) 1972 Ideal Toy Corp. U.S. Pat 3162976 (on back)	**No**
Hair Doodler Cinnamon			X			Yes	©1971 / Ideal Toy Corp / GH-12-H-186 / Hong Kong P (on neck) ©1972 / Ideal Toy Corp/ US Pat 3,162,976 / Other Pat Pend / Hong Kong P. (on back)	**Yes**
Curly Ribbon Cinnamon			X			Yes	Same as Hair Doodler Cinnamon, but "18" at start	**Yes**
First *Tressy*		X			X	Yes	1970 / Ideal Toy Corp / SGH-17-H 161 / Hong Kong (on head) Hong Kong / 1969 Ideal Toy Corp / GH-18 / US PAT 3,162,976 (on back)	**Yes**
Posin' Tressy		X		X		Yes	©1970 / Ideal Toy Corp / SGH-17-H161 / Hong Kong (on head) ©1971 / Ideal Toy Corp / MG-18 / U.S. Pat. 3,162,976 / Other Pat. Pend. / Hong Kong.P. / ©1971 / Ideal Toy Corp / MG / 18 / Hong Kong. P. (on back)	**Yes**
Kerry					X	Yes	13 EYE / ©1970 / Ideal Toy Corp / NGH-18-H-172 / Hong Knog (on neck) 1969 / Ideal Toy Corp / GH-18-US Pat 3,162,976 (on back)	**No**
Brandi			X	X		Yes	1 / ©1971 / Ideal Toy Corp / GHB-18-H-185 / Hong Kong (on neck) ©1971 / Ideal • Toy • Corp / MG-18 / US • Pat. (3 • 162 • 976 / Other • Pat • Pend / Hong • Kong • P (on upper back) ©1971 / Ideal • Toy • Corp / MG-18 / Hong • Kong • P (on lower back)	**No**
Posin' Cricket		X				Yes	1970 / Ideal Toy Corp. / CR-15-H-177 / Hong Kong (on head) 1971 / Ideal Toy Corp / MG-15 / Hong Kong / P (on back)	**No**
Mia		X				Yes	©1970 / Ideal Toy Corp. / NGH-15-H173 / Hong Kong (on neck) Made in Hong Kong / ©1970 / Ideal Toy Corp / GH-15 / 2M5 169-01 (on neck)	**No**
Dina			X	X		Yes	42/ ©1971 / Ideal Toy Corp . GHD-15-H-186 / Hong Kong P. (on neck) ©1971 / Ideal Toy Corp / MG-15 / US Pat 3,162,976 / Other Pat Pend / Hong Kong P (on upper back) ©1971 / Ideal Toy Corp / MG-15 / Hong Kong P. (on lower back)	**No**
Tara		X			X	Yes	Ideal Toy Corp / H-250 / Hong Kong (on neck) Made in Hong Kong / ©1970 Ideal Toy Corp / GH-15 / 2MS 169-01 (on back)	**Was Black**

Outfits

"Sleeper Belles"

"Coat and Hat"

"School Dress"

"Hooded Poncho"

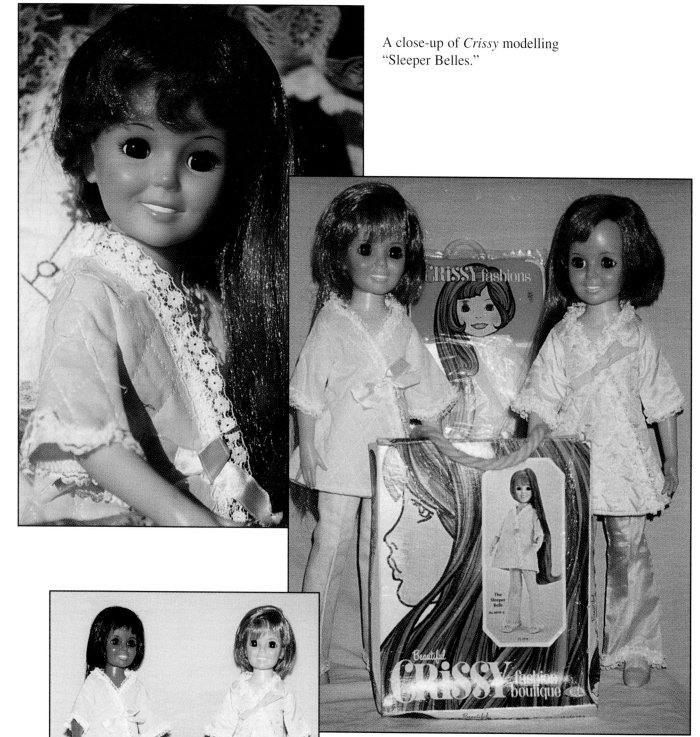

A close-up of *Crissy* modelling "Sleeper Belles."

Two variations of the *Crissy* outfit "Sleeper Belles" are shown with their original packaging. *Photo courtesy of Jennifer Foster.*

Note the difference in the color and type of fabric in two variations of "The Sleeper Belles." *Photo courtesy of Jennifer Foster.*

Crissy Outfits

Two variations of "The Groovy Jumpsuit." "The Groovy Jumpsuit" came as a boxed outfit with a green flowered blouse. When the same jumpsuit came on a card with a green dotted blouse it was called "The Walking Jumpsuit." Note the differences in the color of the fabric and the print design of the material in the blouses. *Photo courtesy of Jennifer Foster.*

Crissy models the lime green, horizontal wale corduroy "Groovy Jumpsuit" which was one of the earliest boxed outfits.

The original packaging for "The Groovy Jumpsuit," #8072-1.

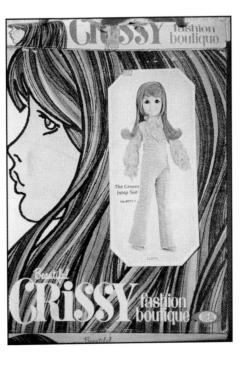

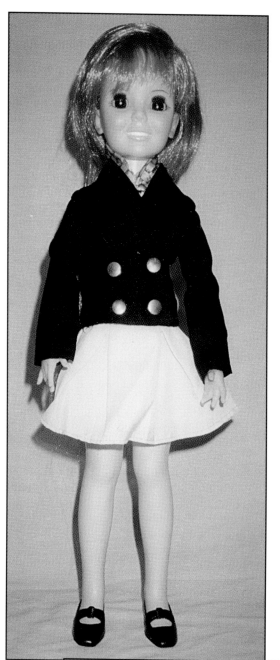

Another of *Crissy*'s early boxed outfits is "The Sporty Blazer". Like a few of the other early boxed outfits, "The Sporty Blazer" may have also occasionally come on a hanger or card package. This outfit is very hard to find. *Photo courtesy of Jennifer Foster.*

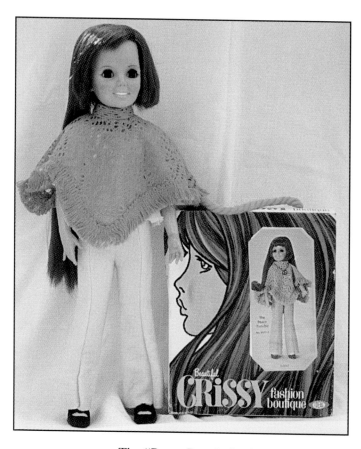

The "Peace Poncho" with a slight variation – the shirt is yellow rather than the usual yellow-green color. *Photo courtesy of Jennifer Foster.*

The "Peace Poncho" with the usual yellow-green shirt. It is #8077-0.

A 1969-1970 Sears Exclusive is the hooded pink plaid "Fun Fur Cape."

The "Fun Fur Cape" is modeled by *Crissy. Photo courtesy of Jay Schefler.*

This darker plaid variation of the "Fun Fur Cape" is a hard to find version of one of *Crissy*'s early boxed outfits. *Photo courtesy of Jennifer Foster.*

Remember those crocheted mini dresses in all of the 1970's needlework magazines? Here is *Crissy* in "With-It Knit."

Crissy wears "With-It Knit," another early boxed outfit. *Photo courtesy of Jennifer Foster.*

The "Turned On Mini" was a boxed outfit. When the same outfit came on a card it was called the "Party Outfit," #8196-8.

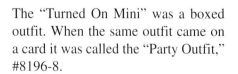

The "City Pants Look" is an example of one of *Crissy*'s early boxed outfits that was later issued on a card. *Photo courtesy of Jennifer Foster.*

Two variations of the "City Pants Look," Note the differenec in the fabric of the pants. *Photo courtesy of Jennifer Foster.*

Another view of the "City Pants Look" and original box. *Photo courtesy of Jennifer Foster.*

Crissy and *Kerry* model one of the early boxed outfits "Seventies Satin," which was available through Sears catalog. This dress was originally sold with a matching long scarf.

The "Seventies Satin" dress is shown with the original box. *Photo courtesy of Jennifer Foster.*

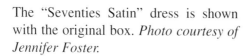

Crissy's Window Box Outfits

The "Lemon Lite" outfit is shown in the original window box packaging.

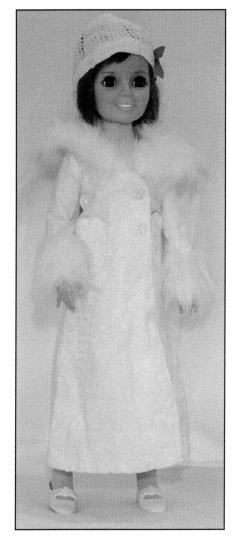

Crissy's "Very Vanilla" ensemble was originally packaged in a window box. *Photo courtesy of Jennifer Foster*

An African-American *Crissy* in the "Lemon Lite" gown.

The delicate shell pink in "Feminine Fancy," #8135-6, sets off the lighter skin tones of this later issue *Crissy*.

Card front from *Crissy* fashions.

"Summer Social" is a very hard to find outfit. It is shown here on *Tressy* and mint-in package. *Photo courtesy of Susan Mobley.*

Card back from 1971 *Crissy* fashions.

A second issue *Crissy* shows off her glorious red mane and outfit #8087-9, "The Jean Machine."

"Jean Machine," #8087-9.

"Grape Drape," #8085-3.

Kerry's coloring radiates in "Grape Drape."

"Drenched Trench," #81083-8.

"Hob Nobber"

"Surf's Up," #8082-0.

"Sleeper Belles"

Card back from 1972 *Crissy* Fashions.

Tressy wearing "Drenched Trench".

Brown haired *Crissy* models the "Hob Nobber."

Crissy wades at the lake shore in "Surf's Up."

"Starshine," #8112-5.

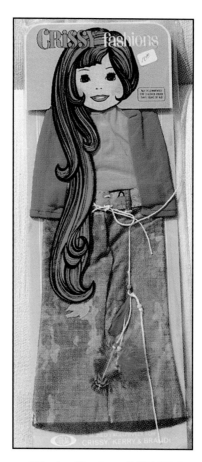

"Funky Feathers," #8117-4.

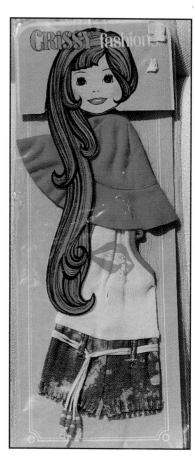

"Lip Smackin," #8114-1.

"Moonshine," #8113-3.

"Skimmer".

"The Dreamer".

Crissy in the patriotic denim trench "Starshine."

Crissy wears "Funky Feathers."

Crissy in "Lip Smackin' Good."

Crissy lets her hair down in "Overall Effect."

"An Overall Effect," #8118-2.

"Double Dip"

Here are some great shots of some of the *Crissy* family outfits that were pictured right on the doll boxes themselves. Someone took the time to arrange the dolls' hair in various styles, which no doubt whetted the appetites of all those countless little girls who were just dying to rip into those boxes and get their hands on all that hair!

Two variations of the *Crissy* Shoe Packs. *Photo courtesy of Jennifer Foster.*

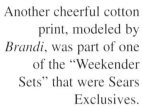

"Patchworker"

Another cheerful cotton print, modeled by *Brandi*, was part of one of the "Weekender Sets" that were Sears Exclusives.

"Gypsy"

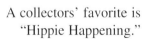

A collectors' favorite is "Hippie Happening."

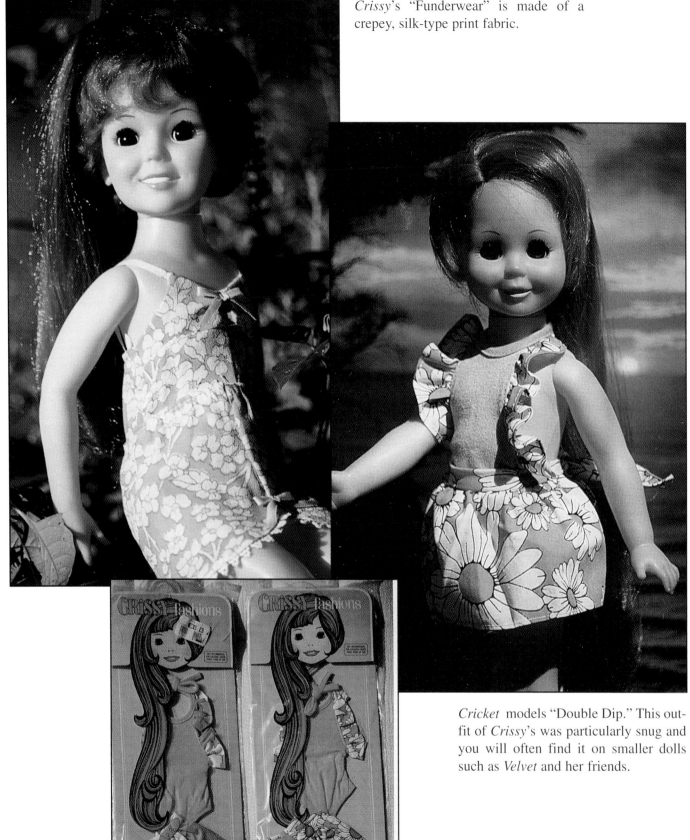

Crissy's "Funderwear" is made of a crepey, silk-type print fabric.

Cricket models "Double Dip." This out-fit of *Crissy*'s was particularly snug and you will often find it on smaller dolls such as *Velvet* and her friends.

Two variations of "Double Dip." The one on the right with smaller green and white daisies and the one on the left in a brown, pink, and orange print. *Photo courtesy of Camilla Holm.*

Crissy's Mystery Outfits

Some outfits have shown up pretty consistently in *Crissy* collections all over the country, but cannot be accounted for in Ideal's records. Could they be Sears or Wards Exclusives, sold for *Crissy* in the store only and not through Christmas catalogs where they would be photographed? Are they substitutions as part of the "Weekender" Sets sold through the Sears Wishbooks? Or are they simply clothing made for *Crissy*-sized dolls by various companies because of her enormous popularity?

This brown crinkle vinyl midi coat is a mystery outfit. It has some similarities to "On the Lamb," but can't be documented as a *Crissy* outfit. If anyone can identify it, please write in.

Another mystery outfit, a long-sleeved sailor-type top with navy cuffed shorts.

A note to all *Crissy* collectors regarding *Crissy* outfits:

Unfortunately, *Crissy* family outfits are not tagged in such a way as to identify them as official *Crissy* creations. Some of the clothing had labels that read "Hong Kong," but none seem to read "*Crissy*."

An outfit sometimes found in *Crissy* collections, but not linked with the Ideal Toy Company – a royal blazer and plaid skirt combination.

Another mystery outfit – a pink corduroy jumper.

Velvet Outfits

The box for *Velvet*'s "School Dress," #8091-1.

Velvet's "School Dress," #8091-1. Notice the mock turtleneck, chain belt, and the use of purples – her signature color.

On the left is shown a darker variation of *Velvet*'s outfit "School Dress." *Photo courtesy of Jennifer Foster.*

Two variations of *Velvet*'s "School Dress." Notice the color of the jumpers and the difference in the materials used for the belts. *Photo courtesy of Jennifer Foster.*

"Baby Doll Pajamas" is one of *Velvet*'s early boxed outfits. *Photo courtesy of Jennifer Foster.*

Velvet in an early boxed outfit "Coat and Hat," #8092-9.

The original box for *Velvet*'s "Coat and Hat," #8092-9.

The "Lace Pants Suit," #8093-7, is another of *Velvet*'s early boxed outfits.

"Checker Check" complete in the original box with the taffeta underslip.

Velvet's "Sailor Suit" boxed outfit.

A country look, complete with a cameo on a black velvet neck ribbon, is modeled by *Dina*. This outfit is called "Checker Check."

The Edwardian look, very popular during these years, is illustrated in "Blazering."

Velvet's "Blazering" boxed outfit.

"On the Lamb," a *Velvet* fashion, was a wet-look crinkled vinyl with a lambs wool-look bodice and sleeves.

"On the Lamb" crinkle vinyl coat and hat with fur trim in the original package.

Card back from
1971 *Velvet*
fashions.

"Play Dots," #8097-8.

"Smarty Pants," # 8095-2.

"Beachnik," #8098-6.

"Kelly Coat,"
#8094-2.

The "Glad Plaid" boxed outfit,
#8096-0.

"Loverly," #8124-0 outfit for *Velvet.*

"Frontier Gear," #8122-4
outfit for *Velvet.*

"Cloud Movement," #8126-5 in the
original packaging.

The card back from 1972
Velvet fashions.

More pictures of *Velvet*'s outfits
on the boxes.

Mia in "Glad Plaid" outfit.

Brandi borrows this stylish cotton peasant dress from her little sister *Dina.* Sometimes called "Pleasantries," sometimes called "Loverly," this was a *Velvet* outfit that could be worn by both the 15-1/2in (and the 17-1/2in [45cm] family dolls}.

Velvet takes a hike in frontier gear.

"Cloud Movement"

Red, white and blue enjoyed
renewed popularity as we
approached the Bicentennial. *Velvet*
is shown wearing "Cloud
Movement."

Shots of
outfits
featured
on
boxes.

Velvet in "Dandy Denims."

"Dandy Denims,"
#8125-7.

Original packaging for "Strawberry Smock."

Blue apples – only in the 1970s! Here is *Tara* wearing "Pulled Together."

"Strawberry Smock"

A *Velvet* shoe pack. *Photo courtesy Jennifer Foster.*

"Pulled Together"

Mia in "Smocked".

"Smocked," #8163-8.

"Short Cuts"

"Blouson Battle"

Mia in a collectors' favorite, "Super Stars."

Mia models an unnamed vinyl skirt and vest ensemble.

The very stylish "Beachnik."

Here is **Tara** in a dress that Cindy Brady would have been proud to wear, "Lemon Hang Up," #8120-8.

Tara models the perfect autumn outfit, "Kinky Kolors."

Dina models what is believed to be one of the generic outfits offered through the Sears catalog. Made for the *Crissy* family dolls. It is easy to see how the body contours of the *Crissy* dolls were designed to show off clothing with very simple lines – long, thin, and straight, without too many curves. So many of these little dresses look completely nondescript on the hanger and seem to come alive when placed on one of the dolls.

Mia models "Ruffled Up," #8099-4.

Mia and *Kerry* model the "Bride" and "Bridesmaid" ensembles that were Sears Exclusives in 1972 and 1973.

Other Velvet outfits not pictured:

"Lace Pants Suit," #8093-7 is bell bottom pants and a tunic top with dark lavender ribbon.

"Baby Doll Pajamas" is a three-piece set with lace trim and lavender shoes.

Please see Rarities chapter for other Velvet outfits identified by Ideal Company stock numbers, but never seen by collectors.

Playsets

Velvet's little sister, too, can). They set her hair. They dried her hair. They brushed her hair. And her hair was a very lovely thing to see. So was Crissy. "Now," they said, "you are ready to talk serious secrets." And she was. And she packed her bag (for a special reason) and she went to see HER.

On the reverse side of the poster *Crissy*'s "Hair Styling Set" is featured in the small center picture.

This 18in (46cm) by 23in (58cm) poster came with the *Look Around Crissy* doll.

The one doll yellow tote, open.

The one doll yellow tote, closed.

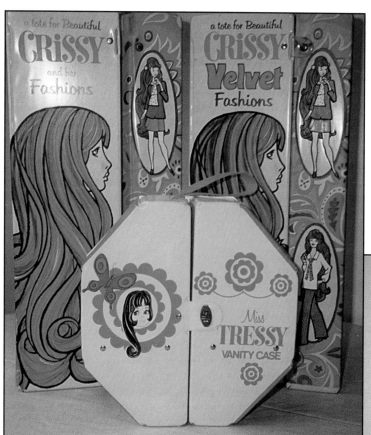

Both of the *Crissy* one doll totes (one with just the *Crissy* name and one that includes Velvet's name) and the "*Miss Tressy* Vanity Case" in the center.

Left to right are the "*Miss Crissy*" case, the hot pink "*Crissy* and *Velvet* Fashion Tote," and the "*Crissy* and Friend Fashion Tote." *Photo courtesy of Wendy Werth.*

All three of the round totes, also called hat boxes by collectors: "*Miss Tressy* Hat Box," "*Miss Crissy*" and "*Miss Velvet*" totes.

A peek inside *Crissy*'s "Beauty Parlor."
Photo courtesy of Jennifer Foster.

The *Crissy* Magic Paper Doll from 1971 came with a 9-1/2in (24cm) cardboard doll, a plastic stand, plastic scissors, and a 48-piece "stay-on" wardrobe. *Photo courtesy of Cindy Sabulis.*

In the background we see the *Tressy – Cricket* and the *Crissy – Velvet* "Fashion Steamer Trunks," both are vinyl with side openings. On either side are two *Crissy – Velvet* "Hair Fashion Totes" and accessories. *Photo courtesy of Wendy Werth.*

Crissy's "Way-Out Wigs," #1033-0, were produced in 1972 and came in three styles.

A truly hard to find item is this *Crissy* Colorform set, #2301, from 1970 which contained stand-up cardboard *Crissy* dolls, each in a different hairstyle, and Colorform outfits. *Photo courtesy of Pauline Yohe.*

The "Way-Out Wig" styles were a blonde and brunette version of an "Afro" (also called a Poodle cut or Poodle Perm) and a longer shag (also called a Fonda, after the hairstyle Jane Fonda wore in the movie *Klute*.

The different styles of the "Way-Out Wigs." *Photo courtesy of Wendy Werth.*

Paper doll sets are: top row, left to right, *Crissy* and *Velvet*, featuring a black doll, *Crissy* Fashion and Hairstyle Boutique, and *Crissy* Magic Paper Doll, and at bottom, The *Crissy* and *Velvet* Coloring Book (stock #1642:59), all by Whitman. *Photo courtesy of Wendy Werth.*

The "*Crissy* Clothes Rack" is pictured here with the "*Crissy* Hair Dryer." In yellow plastic and vinyl, it came with two zip-up garment bags. *Photo courtesy of Wendy Werth.*

Crissy's "Hair Dryer" set "hums and blows like the real thing." *Photo courtesy of Jennifer Foster.*

To the right of the *Crissy* and *Velvet* paper dolls is the set entitled *Crissy – Paper Doll With Fun Fashions*, published by Whitman. *Photo courtesy of Jennifer Foster.*

Great shots of "*Crissy*'s Beauty Parlor," showing the accessories. Many of us have seen the set at flea markets and not known what it was. The braiding device pictured on the box appears to be made of metal, when in reality it was lavender plastic. *Photo courtesy of Cindy Sabulis.*

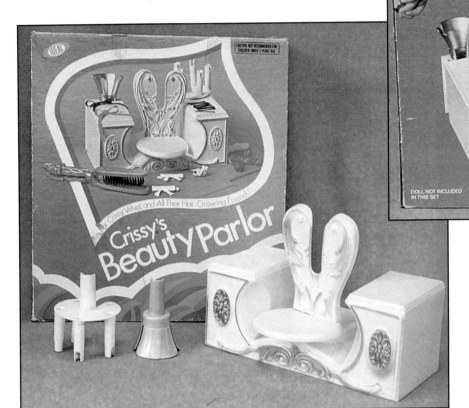

Here is another hard to find item – the "*Velvet* and *Crissy* Shopping Spree Game," #2014-9, from 1970, in which *Crissy* and *Velvet* receive money for allowance and good grades, and run through the game board spending it all on fashion accessories and record albums. *Photo courtesy of Jay Schefler.*

Original Catalog Outfits

49 C 30752—Shpg. wt. 5 oz............$3.99

3 Hooded cape with fur-look trim, pompons.
49 C 30751—Shpg. wt. 5 oz............$3.99
Note: Dolls not included with outfits.

4 Hair Care Kit. Incl. all setting, styling needs.
49 C 30749—Shipping weight 6 oz......$1.99

As in any area of doll collecting, old catalogs pages give us the opportunity to see original dolls' outfits with all of their matching accessories, and help us to identify obscure playsets and items that are hard to find today.

These pages also let us see the great photography of absolutely mint dolls when they were brand new and almost untouched. After finding many examples of "pre-loved" and "well played with" dolls from a bygone era, you may look at the perfectly pristine faces staring up at you from an old Wish Book, with their radiant cheek blush and glossy hair, and say "Oh my gosh! Is that what they're supposed to look like?"

These Sears Exclusives Outfits were offered in 1969, *Crissy*'s first year: yellow pajamas and quilted robe with blue lace trim (#2), plaid wool poncho with pink fur trim (#3) and the organza gown that many collectors would like to get their hands on (#1). The gown is done in gold and pink stripes with metallic accents and maribou feather trim. It was not sold separately, but came with the *Crissy* doll, along with her first issue orange lace dress, hairstyling booklet, and comb. Note the haircare kit #4 on the bottom of the page.

This Montgomery Wards Exclusive is something most collectors have not even heard of. Introduced as "*Joann*, a charming young friend for *Crissy*," she is extremely difficult to find, and , technically, a missing link to any complete *Crissy* collection. About an inch shorter than *Velvet*, and three inches shorter than *Crissy*, she is a grow hair doll with ash blonde hair and blue eyes. *Joann* is shown in her original red dress on the right and mod-elling Wards Exclusive *Velvet* outfits on the left.

From left to right, in a 1970 Sears' catalog advertisement, are: 1) *Velvet*'s pajama and robe set, 2) *Velvet*'s coat and hat set, 3) *Crissy*'s satin mini shown with the matching scarf, 4) "Sleeper Belles," 5) *Crissy*'s poncho set, 6) "Turned On Mini," 7) plaid wool hooded poncho.

The 1971 Sears Wish Book shows that year's line up of *Crissy* dolls, including a black *Tressy*, and a *Cricket* in a slightly different shade of hair than we are used to seeing. The "Shoe Wardrobe" at the bottom of the page was available for $1.89.

To the right, wearing yellow, we see Mattel's answer to the *Crissy* family, 11in (28cm) *Valerie*. Today very hard to find, she was an adorable grow hair doll with the "Small Talk" face mold.

The *Crissy* and *Velvet* outfits on the left are all familiar to collectors, but the center of the page shows the "*Crissy* Hair Dryer," a real sign of the times with its bonnet attachment and butterfly motif. The ad claims that it "really works." The vinyl two-doll case is shown at the bottom right for $3.99, along with an "Accessory Trunk" for $5.99, and the "Clothes Rack" for $4.99 which came with two garment bags. All of this was featured in the Sears 1971 Wish Book.

In 1971 Sears shows great photography of *Movin' Groovin' Crissy* and *Movin' Groovin'* (*Posin'*) *Tressy*.

The top of this page from the 1972 Sears Wish Book shows some hard to find *Crissy* and *Velvet* outfits that were sold under the titles "Go Mix & Match" for *Velvet* and "Weekender" for *Crissy*. It is difficult to say who, over the years, manufactured these outfits and it is believed there were some variations in color and style. *Cricket* models three outfits at the top left: a checked sundress with three yellow flowers, blue coveralls with a yellow appliqued apple, and a green jumper with a blouse. At the top right, *Tressy* models a red sailor suit, a robe, and a sheer negligee.

The bottom outfits are all familiar packaged outfits: "Blazering," "On the Lamb," "Dandy Denims," and "Frontier Gear" for *Velvet* and "Blazering," "Very Vanilla," "Funky Feathers," and "Starshine" for *Crissy*. *Crissy*'s "Blazering" and "Very Vanilla" are currently very hard to find. "Very Vanilla" was one of the early boxed outfits, and was a white maxi coat with fur trim and a matching cloche hat.

The 1973 Sears Christmas catalog offers collectors some insight into the "Swirla Curler" and "Beauty Braid" devices. Original price of *Swirla Curler Crissy* was $8.44, and the price for *Velvet* with Beauty Braider was $7.97.

Also featured are *Brandi* and *Dina*, which sold for $5.97. "Except for their tans and their sun-kissed hair, Brandi and Dina are just like their Eastern realtives..." Also included in this ad are *Cinnamon* with Hair Doodler for $4.44, and a "*Crissy* Carry Case," outfits and the "Beauty Parlor" for $5.97.

Sears' 1972 catalog featured the Exclusive Wedding Sets, sold with *Cricket* and *Tressy*, each $9.99, or alone, without the dolls for $2.08 per outfit.

In the right hand panel, we see the "Crissy Hair Setting Kit" with "hot rollers" for $3.49, the "Hair Accessory Kit" for $1.99, and one style of Crissy's "Way Out Wigs" in the long shag or Fonda style.

The Sears Exclusive "Bride" and "Bridesmaid" Gift Sets were offered in the 1973 Wish Book with *Movin' Groovin' Tressy* and *Cricket* for a (now) heart-breaking price of $6.77.

First *Baby Crissy,* with the longer hair and pink dress appeared in the 1973 Sears' Wish Book.

Another layette for *Baby Crissy* is pictured in a 1975 Montgomery Wards' catalog.

The beads twirl and twist Crissy's hair into dozens of styles. Abt. 17½ in. tall. Wt. 1 lb. 11 oz.
48 G 10218—White Crissy doll.............9.44
48 G 10219—Black Crissy doll.............9.44

Save 1.55. Crissy is only 7.89 when you buy her with stylish outfits, (9) below. Wt. 2 lbs. 2 oz.
48 G 10296—White Crissy with Outfits.....13.88
48 G 10294—Black Crissy with Outfits.....13.88

braided, piled high or in a ponytail. For the country-look, she wears crisp plaid pinafore dress, lavender like her daisies. About 15 in. tall. Ship. wt. 1 lb. 11 oz.
48 G 10220—Velvet doll only...............9.44

Save 1.55. Velvet is only 7.89 when you buy her with pretty outfits, (10) below. Wt. 2 lbs. 2 oz.
48 G 10297—Velvet with Outfits............12.88

4 Outfits for Crissy 5⁹⁹ set

9 Smart wardrobe for Crissy, other 17½-18 in. fashion dolls. Stylish long skirt with blouse, lace-trimmed pj's, mini with stripe trim, layered-look pantsuit, apron. Colors, fabrics may vary.
48 G 11058—Outfits only. Ship. wt. 7 oz.....5.99

4 Outfits for Velvet 4⁹⁹ set

10 Latest styles for Velvet, other 15-in. fashion dolls. Long skirt and body suit for evenings at home, frilly pajamas, tunic with shorts, apron, dressy pantsuit. Colors and fabrics may vary.
48 G 11059—Outfits only. Ship. wt. 7 oz........4.99

Montgomery Wards' 1974 Christmas catalog offered extra outfits for *Crissy* and *Velvet*.

Pictured to the right of this photo are ten outfits made for *Crissy, Velvet,* and of course, all their friends. These were offered through the Alden's 1974 Christmas catalog.

In 1975 Montgomery Wards pictured six ensembles for *Crissy* and *Velvet*.

Both white and African-American *Crissys'* are pictured in the 1976 Sears Wish Book.

$16⁸⁷ each

Life-size, 2-foot Baby Crissy has hair that "grows" to her shoulders

(7 and 8) Baby Crissy. Pull her hair to make it "grow"; pull string in back of neck to shorten it.
BODY. DETAILING: 24 in. tall. Soft vinyl foam skin . . . baby almost feels alive. Jointed arms, legs to pose her. White doll (7) has auburn rooted hair; black doll (8) has black rooted hair. Sparkling eyes.
CLOTHES. ACCESSORIES: Lavender dress and pants. This life-size doll can wear real baby clothes, too.
FOR AGES: 5 to 10 years.
ORDERING INFO: Shipping weight each 5 lbs.
(7)   79 N 31658C—White Baby Crissy $16.87
(8)   79 N 31659C—Black Baby Crissy 16.87

18-inch Dearest
Just listen **$1**
to her cry

(1) Dearest Infant sounds when you tilt BODY. DETAILING: legs and head attach body . . . prop her in rooted hair. Open-and CLOTHES. ACCESS trimmed pajama top FOR AGES: 4 to 10 ye ORDER INFO: Order 49 N 31693—Shpg. wt.

(2) Dress for Dea white check dress wi White diaper, knit bo ORDERING INFO: Do 49 N 32584—Shpg. wt.

(3) Coverall for D red knit coverall with ORDERING INFO: Do 49 N 32585—Shpg. wt.

The 1974 dolls are pictured in the 1974 Montgomery Wards Christmas catalog, along with one of the layettes offered for *Baby Crissy*.

She's life size! Baby Crissy
with growing hair
Save 2.48
12⁹⁶
Only   when you
buy her 4-outfit layette, too!

Doll separately 15⁴⁴

aby Crissy is adorable, a cuddly, lifelike baby 24 . tall. You've seen her on TV. She's soft, hug- able and lightweight, her jointed vinyl body is ed with plastic foam. Petal-soft baby skin feels al. Pretty auburn hair "grows" from short to long her hair string. Baby Crissy is

The World of Crissy

Beautiful Dolls with hair that "grows"
Crissy with Twirly Beads
Velvet with Swirly Daisies

Your choice   **7⁸⁹** when you buy their
only   4-outfit wardrobe, tool

Dolls separately 9⁴⁴ each

7 8 Crissy and Velvet are exquisite beauties with lifelike vinyl heads, delicately tinted features, lovely

Rarities

Never Hit the Shelves

Prototypes of a beautiful *Baby Velvet* were made, but the doll was never mass-produced and made available in stores. She has a distinctly *Velvet*-style face, but with chubbier cheeks, blonde pigtails and large lavender eyes. All vinyl, she was 20in (51cm) tall and had a grow-hair feature.

It is believed that the following *Crissy* outfits were made, but never hit the store shelves:
#8194-3 Lavender dress
#8195-0 Satin Coat
#8197-6 Nightgown (long with ruffled neck)
#8198-4 Grey Striped Pant Suit
#8199-2 Evening Gown (described as more like a coat, and having long sleeves)

If anyone feels they own these outfits, please contact the author through the publisher.

No collector that I have spoken to has ever seen the following *Velvet* outfits that were listed in an Ideal catalog:
#8190-1 Overalls and Blouse
#8188-5 Bathing Suit and Tee
#8189-3 Plaid Pajamas
#8191-9 Coat and Head Scarf
#8192-7 Apron Dress
#8193-5 Long Strawberry Dress
(# unknown) Blackberries Maxi Jumper with a body suit underneath

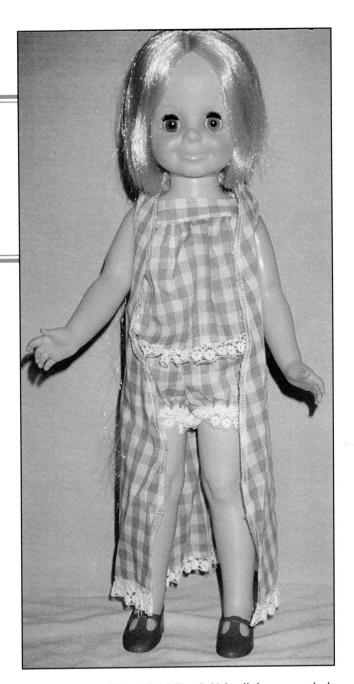

This "Odd-Eyed *Velvet*" has one dark and one light (almost pink) violet eye. No value has been established for this doll. *Photo courtesy of Jennifer Foster.*

Brown haired *Crissy* is believed to have been produced within the first year. This hair color variation makes for a rare and sought-after doll. *Doll courtesy of Pauline Yohe.*

Another beautiful brown haired *Crissy*. *Doll courtesy of Camilla Holm.*

For the *Crissy* version of the *Velvet* outfit "Blazering," Ideal seems to have used the same blazer that was used for *Velvet*'s outfit, making it a bit snug for *Crissy* and her friends. *Crissy*'s "Blazering" is just like *Velvet*'s, but with a floor-length or Maxi skirt, and is considered hard to find by collectors.

Wonderful comparison of the tones and colors in both a standard *Crissy* (left) and a true brown haired *Crissy* (right), sent in by Paula Carranza. As you can see, a true brown haired *Crissy* has no reddish cast to her hair.

Green-eyed *Velvet* is a true rarity. How she got her green eyes – whether it was a factory error or a short-term experiment – no one seems to know. I know of only two in the hands of collectors. *Photo courtesy of Wendy Werth.*

There are only a few of these "Pale Face *Crissys*," shown here in the center, that have shown up in the collectors' arena. Actually the entire body and limbs of the doll as well as her face, are noticeably paler than a standard *Crissy* doll. This uniform paleness eliminates any theories of a doll that may have been left out in the sun. Collectors report that the vinyl seems to be of a lighter weight than the vinyl on a standard *Crissy*. The doll's makeup is less pronounced, suggesting that she is a later doll. *Photograph courtesy of Pauline Yohe.*

On the left is *Joann* by NASCO. *Doll courtesy of Bev Hagaman.*

Hard to Find:

In polling collectors, the following items have been determined to be hard to find:

Black 1st issue *Crissy*

Other black *Crissys* in general, except for *Magic Hair Crissy* and the 1983 reissue.

The Porcelain *Crissy* from Dollspart, 1980

1st issue black *Baby Crissy*

2ns issue black *Baby Crissy* (more rigid vinyl)

Black *Cinnamon*

Any black *Velvet*

Tressy's stretch headband

Tara

The *Crissy* outfit "The Groovy Jumpsuit" (see page 51)

The *Crissy* outfit "With It Knit" (see page 54)

Sears Exclusive pink Plaid Poncho (see page 53)

Crissy outfit "Summer Social" (see page 58)

Crissy outfit "Turned on Mini" (see page 54)

Crissy outfit "Blazering" (see page 96)

Velvet "Coat and Hat" (see page 70)

Velvet outfit "School Dress" (see page 69)

The two doll tote

Way-Out Wig sets

Crissy Colorforms

Satin Mini

Sewing patterns made for *Crissy*

An extremely rare doll, this green-eyed *Mia* on the right shows a distinctly different eye color form the bright blue of a standard *Mia* on the left. This is the only example of a green-eyed *Mia* that I have come across to date. *Photo courtesy of Paula Carranza.*

Rare:

In polling collectors, the following items have been determined to be rare:

Talky Crissy with back butterfly

Black Look Around *Velvet*

Black *Tressy*

Blue-eyed *Cricket*

Green-eyed *Velvet*

Crissy outfit "Lemon Lite" (see page 57)

Crissy outfit "Very Vanilla" (see page 57)

Crissy outfit "Lemon Hang Up" (see page 79)

Crissy outfit "The Bold Blazer" (also called "Sporty Blazer") (see page 52)

Joann doll

Sears Exclusive organdy striped gown with Maribou Feathers

A true brown haired *Crissy*

Tressy Hair Care Kit

Green-eyed *Mia*

Child-sized "Fashion Tote"

Miss Crissy and *Miss Velvet* Shoulder Bag

All 1974 outfits

All *Cinnamon* outfits

Pale face *Crissy*

Very hard to find and very much in demand is this striking outfit, "Turned On Mini," which was a Sears' 1970 Exclusive. Complete with gold fish net stockings and pink satin ribbon trim and lining on the sleeves, it is very '70s and anything but nondescript.

Although not manufactured by Ideal, *Joann* was introduced as a "charming young friend for *Crissy*" in a 1970 Christmas catalog and is part of the collectors' frenzy for those who know about her. She has two stationary buttons, one on each side of her head, and her grow hair mechanism seems to operate on a pull down/retract up tension spring, similar to the way a window shade works. She is 14-1/2in (37cm) tall, all vinyl, with ash blonde hair, very light green eyes, and is marked "NASCO ©" on the back of her neck.

Sewing for Crissy

The patterns I have uncovered for *Crissy* Family dolls include the following by Simplicity:

#8519 – (1969)

#9138 – (1970)

#9698 – (1971)

#5276 – (1972)

Thanks so much to Frances Waters and her sister Doris Rickert, who share my love of dressing dolls, for their help!

Simplicity #9138 was suitable for "teen dolls such as *Velvet* 15-1/2in (39cm) and Beautiful *Crissy* 17-1/2in (45cm) and included patterns for a dress, blouse, tunic, skirt, vest, pants, baby-doll pajamas, and a poncho.

Simplicity #8519 should have been enlarged for Marcia Brady herself. A great empire style dress with bell sleeves was offered along with bell bottom pants, a long vest, tie waisted blazer, halter top, the perfect 70's jumper and a fringed Charleston dress. It was "suitable for 17-1/2in (45cm) teenage dolls such as Beautiful *Crissy*." (1969).

Simplicity #9698 offered a peasant dress, maxi cape, short and vest set, knickers, palazzo pants jumpsuit, and a bride dress and veil.

Johana Gast Anderton's *Sewing For Twentieth Century Dolls* includes patterns for Beautiful *Crissy* by Ideal.

Simplicity #5276 included a sailor suit, short and shift set, long halter dress, wrap-around pants skirt, mini dress and blazer. Dolls listed on the pattern envelope were *Velvet, Look Around Velvet, Talky Velvet, Dina, Crissy, Look Around Crissy, Talky Crissy,* and *Brandi.* (1972).

The August 1979 issue of *Doll World* ran a four page spread on sewing for *Crissy*, with patterns and directions for making a bridal gown and veil. The article was written by Ruth Gwartney.

The May issue of *Doll Designs* magazine featured a classic dress pattern for *Crissy* by Evelyn Leybourne.

In 1972 Virginia Lakin's Doll Knitting and Crochet Books # 10 and # 11 featured patterns for the *Crissy* family.

The Spring 1980 issue of *National Doll World Omnibook* featured *Velvet* on its cover, and inside a pattern for a Victorian outfit for her.

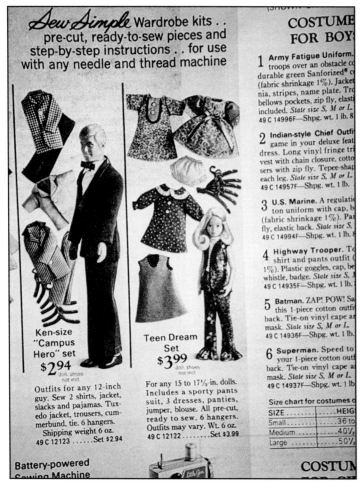

This "Teen Dream Sew Simple Set" of pre-cut, ready to sew pieces fit the *Crissy* Family of dolls and was available in the Sears 1973 Wish Book for $3.99.

This beautiful bridal set was made for Susan Mobley's *Crissy* by her aunt Edna Leonard in 1972. Note the perfect hems and tiny ruffles of tulle that peak out from underneath. *Photo courtesy of Susan Mobley.*

When collectors sew for *Crissy*, she is frequently redressed as a bride. This dress and strand of pearls are factory made but the veil was made by Camilla Holm. The long and simple lines of this bridal ensemble are perfect for *Crissy*, but she can wear any style well.

The long straight lines of the *Crissy* family dolls make them favorites to sew for and redress. This dress makes *Crissy* look as though she is straight off the set of "Gunsmoke". *Photo courtesy of Camilla Holm.*

Portrait Gallery

Brandi

The little mothers who owned life-size *Baby Crissy* could shop for her in real baby departments.

African-American *Magic Hair Crissy* displays her warm mahogany skin tones and her vivid black hair. Notice how complimentary the deep terra cotta lip color is.

Crissy

The fair Irish lass, *Kerry*.

Dina

Wendy Werth's collection.

Susan Mobley, Christmas morning, 1970, with her *Crissy* doll in the "Sporty Blazer" outfit, and the same doll as she appears today. I am amazed at the wonderful condition of this brown haired *Crissy*. Obviously, Susan is adept at taking care of her "stuff". Although I was always known to play well with others and never sang at the supper table or ran with scissors, I didn't take care of my "stuff" as well as Susan. *Photo courtesy of Susan Mobley.*

The same brown haired *Crissy* doll that appears in the Christmas photos on page 107 and 108. Susan obviously took very good care of her doll. *Photo courtesy of Susan Mobley.*

Three decades of delight can be chronicled in these two photos of Tara Wood and sister Paula Carranza as they appear in 1970 and again in 1997 with the same prized *Crissy* doll and an additional mint and beautiful example. Tara and Paula would like to dedicate this page to the person who bought them this *Crissy* doll, their mother, with this quote: "We would like to dedicate this to the person who gave us life, love, and happiness...you will be forever in our hearts and in our memories. We love you, Ma." Paula and Tara in 1970.

Tara and Paula in 1997.

This Diana Ross doll, marked 1969 – Ideal Toy Corp. also shares the same body mold as *Crissy* She has no grow hair feature. *Photo courtesy of Wendy Werth.*

Crissy Price Guide

In this book, the values have been determined by polling a number of *Crissy* collectors, documenting actual sales, and then taking an average. This takes into consideration the variations of prices in different areas of the country.

All prices in this book are for dolls and items that are mint in box or mint on card.

For mint dolls that are not absolutely complete and without a box, take off about 40%. For dolls in played with condition and without and original outfit, take off about 80%.

			I Want	I Have
First Issue *Crissy* with floor length hair (1968-69)	White	$110	❑	❑
	Black	$180	❑	❑
Second Issue *Crissy* (1969) with knee length hair	White	$75	❑	❑
	Black	$125	❑	❑
Third Issue *Crissy* (1969-70) with turquoise dress	White	$75	❑	❑
Movin' Groovin' Crissy (1971) orange midi dress, orange boots	White	$60	❑	❑
	Black	$100	❑	❑
Talky Crissy with side pull string	White	$90	❑	❑
Look Around Crissy (1972) green plaid taffeta	White	$70	❑	❑
	Black	$110	❑	❑
Swirla Curler Crissy (1973) red-orange plaid jumper and curler apparatus	White	$65	❑	❑
	Black	$105	❑	❑
Twirley Beads Crissy (1974) pink check maxi dress	White	$65	❑	❑
	Black	$85	❑	❑
Magic Hair Crissy (1977) short hair with hair piece attachments	White	$55	❑	❑
		$80	❑	❑
New Issue *Crissy* (1983) either dress	White	$45	❑	❑
	Black	$55	❑	❑
Porcelain *Crissy* by Dollspart		$180	❑	❑
First *Baby Crissy* (1980) in pink, salmon, or lavender		$100	❑	❑
Second *Baby Crissy* (1980) white swimsuit	White	$80	❑	❑
	Black	$115	❑	❑
Hairless *Baby Crissy* (1983)		$110	❑	❑
First *Velvet* (1969-70) purple velvet jumper		$50	❑	❑
First Black *Velvet* (1970-71) lavender corduroy jumper		$105	❑	❑
Movin' Groovin' Velvet (1971) two tone pink low waisted dress	White	$50	❑	❑
	Black	$105	❑	❑
Talky Velvet (1971) red plaid taffeta dress	White	$90	❑	❑
Look Around Velvet (1972) red plaid taffeta dress	White	$60	❑	❑
	Black	$145	❑	❑
Beauty Braider Velvet (1973) white and lavender mini dress, braiding device	White	$60	❑	❑
	Black	$115	❑	❑
Swirly Daisy Velvet (1974) purple and pink plaid dress, daisy chain	White	$60	❑	❑
	Black	$130	❑	❑
New Issue *Velvet* (1980s) white cotton dress	White	$40	❑	❑
	Black	$55	❑	❑
First *Cinnamon* (1971) orange and white dot dress	White	$65	❑	❑
Second *Cinnamon* (1973) Hair Doodler, orange and white tops and shorts	White	$60	❑	❑
	Black	$115	❑	❑
Third *Cinnamon* (Curly Ribbons) (1974) denim bibs	White	$70	❑	❑
	Black	$125	❑	❑
First *Tressy* (1969) gold and white dress	White	$95	❑	❑
	Black	$165	❑	❑
Second *Tressy* (1971) aqua satin mini dress	White	$70	❑	❑

Kerry (1971)	$70	❏	❏
Brandi (1972)	$70	❏	❏
Harmony (1972)	$85	❏	❏
Harmony outfits, mint on card	$35 Ea.	❏	❏
Mia (1971)	$60	❏	❏
First *Cricket* (1971) orange and white diagonal check, brown eyes	$80	❏	❏
Blue-eyed *Cricket*	$180	❏	❏
Dina (1972)	$70	❏	❏
Tara (1976)	$140	❏	❏
Crissy's Early Boxed Outfits	$35 Ea.	❏	❏
Crissy's Carded Outfits, not including the rare ones	$18 Ea.	❏	❏
Velvet's Early Boxed Outfits	$25 Ea.	❏	❏
Velvet's Carded Outfits, not including the rare ones	$18 Ea.	❏	❏
One Doll Yellow Tote	$20	❏	❏
Miss Tressy Vanity Case	$40	❏	❏
Steamer Trunks	$40	❏	❏
Hair Fashion Totes	$28	❏	❏
Miss *Crissy* Case	$28	❏	❏
Crissy and *Velvet* Fashion Tote	$30	❏	❏
Crissy and Friend Fashion Tote	$30	❏	❏
Hat Boxes	$35	❏	❏
Paper Dolls, uncut	$25	❏	❏
Crissy and *Velvet* Coloring Book	$22	❏	❏
Crissy's Beauty Parlor	$45	❏	❏
Crissy's Clothes Rack	$32	❏	❏
Shopping Spree Game	$30	❏	❏

Rarities

Tressy's Stretch Headband	$12	❏	❏
Crissy outfit "The Groovy Jumpsuit"	$33	❏	❏
Crissy outfit "With It Knit"	$43	❏	❏
Sears Exclusive Pink Plaid Poncho	$28	❏	❏
Crissy outfit "Summer Social"	$36	❏	❏
Crissy outfit "Turned on Mini"	$45	❏	❏
Crissy outfit "Blazering"	$50	❏	❏
Velvet outfit "Coat and Hat"	$25	❏	❏
Velvet outfit "School Dress"	$25	❏	❏
The two Doll Tote	$35	❏	❏
Way-Out Wig Sets	$30	❏	❏
Crissy Colorforms	$25	❏	❏
Satin Mini	$35	❏	❏
Sewing Patterns Made for *Crissy*	$12	❏	❏

About the Author

Not many people know this, but Carla actually went to college with *Crissy* in the late 1970s. Carla is pictured here with both *Crissy* and *Kerry* during a ski club trip in 1978. Carla remembers *Crissy* as "a bit on the quiet side, but well liked and with an endless variety of hairstyles."

This is Carla's second book on the subject of modern dolls, following her first book **Modern Doll Rarities**. In addition, she has authored over 100 magazine articles on dolls and other baby-boomer era toys. Married to attorney Richard Cross, she is the proud mother of six children: Tiffin, Bria, Lacelynn, Jonnica, Dustin, and Jamison.